The National Waterfront Museum

The story of Wales's industry and innovation

Amgueddfa
Genedlaethol
y Glannau
STORI DIWYDIANT A
BLAENGAREDD CYMRU

National
Waterfront
Museum
WALES' STORY OF
INDUSTRY & INNOVATION

The National Waterfront Museum is a partnership between National Museum Wales and the City and County of Swansea. The Museum was made possible by the European Regional Development Fund, European Union Objective One, the Heritage Lottery Fund, the Wales Tourist Board, the Welsh Assembly Government and the Welsh Development Agency.

Generous funding was received from Admiral, Barclays Plc, William Burgess, Community Union, Corus Strip Products UK, GC Gibson Charitable Trust, the Simon Gibson Charitable Trust, The Foyle Foundation, The Lloyds TSB Foundation for England and Wales, The Llysdinam Trust, The Pilgrim Trust, The SR & PH Southall Charitable Trust, Swansea City Waste Disposal Company Ltd, the Welsh Assembly Government's Aggregates Levy Sustainability Fund for Wales, the Weston Family and The Wolfson Foundation.

Valuable support has also been received from The Atlantic Foundation, Deborah Services Limited, Christopher Gridley, History Makers Supporters, Dr Margaret Berwyn Jones, The Oakdale Trust, South Wales Evening Post, The Trusthouse Charitable Foundation, Western Power Distribution, Dr Hilary Lloyd Yewlett and two anonymous donors.

ISBN: 0 7200 0561 2

Text: Richard Keen
Editor: Mari Gordon
Design: Third Millennium Publishing,
an imprint of Third Millennium Information Ltd
Printing: Printer Trento, Italy

Contents

An introduction to the National Waterfront Museum   4

The industrialisation of Wales   7

Early industrial developments   9
  Over land   10
  Over water   13

People's lives   15
  Workers' homes   15
  Health   15
  A woman's work   16
  Uprising and unrest   19

Religion   20

Industries   25
  Metals   25
  Slate   33
  Textiles   38
  Coal   40

Transport   46
  Rivers and canals   46
  Ports and harbours   48
  Railways   50
  The Twentieth Century   53
  Between two world wars   53
  The second half of the twentieth century   55
  The transformation of the landscape   56

Information for Visitors   62

Glossary   64

* The National Waterfront Museum is designed around fifteen themed exhibition areas, which are reflected in this book. Interspersed with the chapters, you will come across sections with more information on the themes as they are explored in the Museum

An introduction to the National Waterfront Museum

Welcome to the National Waterfront Museum. This is a special museum, the result of years of imagining, developing and planning by National Museum Wales. We wanted a new way of telling Wales's industrial history and explaining how Wales became the world's first industrial nation. After wide consultation, Swansea was chosen as the location for the new museum, a city whose industrial history illustrates many of the stories we wanted to tell, and a partnership was formed between the National Museum and the City and County of Swansea.

A new kind of museum experience

Once the waterfront location was chosen, we had the opportunity to think about what kind of museum we wanted. This was a chance to be fresh and innovative – a clean slate. We already knew that there would be no entry fee: the Welsh Assembly Government enabled the National Museum to drop entry charges in 2001. With no need for ticket desks or barriers, this museum has four ways in: you can enter, and explore, as you please.

We had a choice from over 100,000 artefacts relating to Wales's industrial past.

© James Brittain

© James Brittain

There are over 1,000 items on display, exploring fifteen different themes such as energy and the land. However, the museum looks at people and communities, not just the objects. The displays will change and will be constantly refreshed, always illuminating different aspects of people's lives. Also, although museums are usually about the past, you will find that your visit is as much about the present and the future.

The building: bridging the new and the old

The Museum is housed in a remarkable building. There are two elements: an original dockside warehouse from 1901, stripped back to reveal the elegant structure, and the new, specially built modern slate and glass structure. The two aspects are linked by an airy walkway, which then extends from the Museum, reuniting the city with the waterfront. This partnership of the past with the future creates a building full of history, light and details that will delight and surprise you.

You'll have noticed the changes of colour in the Welsh slate cladding outside. The horizontal bands reflect layers of sediments laid down millions of years ago. These layers were compressed over time to form slate, then pushed up at an angle by movement of the earth's plates. This created the vertical cleaving we see in slate, which is exploited by the skilled craftsmen who 'dress' slate by hand today.

The building's design also exploits more recent historical evidence of the site's industrial archaeology. The form of the new building follows the old railway lines that led to the dockside buildings. Inside and in the garden you'll find the lines of the original tracks and sidings that once carried Welsh raw materials to be exported to the rest of the world.

The industrialisation of Wales

The industrialisation of Wales was directly linked to the geology and topography of the land. Its naturally rich deposits of coal, metal ores, slate, stone and clays, together with plentiful water power (later supplemented and largely overtaken by steam) drove its transformation from an agricultural to an industrial economy from the mid-eighteenth century onwards. But Wales's industrial history can be traced as far back as the Bronze Age. Copper is known to have been mined at the Great Orme, near Llandudno, before 1860BC, while the Romans mined gold at Pumsaint, near Lampeter, from around AD77 until the end of the fourth century. In 1248, coal was worked at Neath by the local Cistercian community, and by the sixteenth century iron furnaces were being worked in north and south Wales.

At the start of the eighteenth century, Wales was sparsely populated. The largest town was Carmarthen, with a population of less than 4,000, and there were few places with more than 1,500 people. Many towns were of medieval origin, most with a crumbling castle in or near their centres.

Most people depended on agriculture and lived in tenanted farms and cottages or in small market towns. People lived their lives at a local level, with the services they needed – such as a blacksmith, corn miller or saddler – available close by. Few would have travelled far from their home settlement. Generally, with the exception of some of the larger estates, the land was poor and inefficiently worked.

By the middle of the nineteenth century, industrialisation was well under way across Wales, and many towns were evolving into significant urban centres. The country was changing, as more people worked in industry than in agriculture, making Wales the world's first industrial nation.

Drawing of Flintshire coal miners, 1689

ENERGY

Crown copyright: Royal Commission on the Ancient and Historical Monuments of Wales

Wylfa Nuclear Power Station in Anglesey

The generation and use of energy is absolutely vital to daily life. Throughout history, the need to improve the production of energy has driven much of our technological progress. Muscle power has been enhanced by the use of wheeled vehicles or a block-and-pulley system. Water power has been used extensively across Wales, from the most basic waterwheel to the gigantic hydroelectric pumped storage power station at Dinorwig.

Coal was the main fuel that powered thousands of steam engines across the length and breadth of Wales. Some steam engines were of massive proportions, such as the engine that

once drove the ventilating fan at the Navigation Colliery in Crumlin. Llandarcy Oil Refinery was built in the 1920s, as the demand for oil-based energy increased, and eventually it was linked via a pipeline to the deep-sea oil terminal at Milford Haven.

In 1969, the Wylfa Nuclear Power Station in Anglesey was the largest in the world, with a total output of over 1,000 megawatts. Today, in response to concerns over pollution, wind farms are appearing across the landscape and there is an increasing need to build houses with high levels of sustainability.

The Green House at St Fagans National History Museum explores ideas in sustainable living

Early industrial developments

Before the Industrial Revolution, industries in Wales were small-scale and scattered. There were charcoal-burning iron furnaces at Dolgun near Dolgellau, at Bersham near Wrexham and in the Angidy Valley, an off-shoot of the Wye Valley. Metals were mined at Cwmystwyth near Aberystwyth and on Halkyn Mountain, and coal was mined on a small scale near the south Wales coast. In river valleys, small textile mills were established, while weaving was mostly carried out at or near the homesteads.

However, some places began to show signs of industrial development. The first copper-smelting works in Wales had been opened in 1584 at Aberdulais, near Neath, and the locality would later emerge as an important focus of industrial activity, largely owing to the efforts of Sir Humphrey Mackworth, one of the early mining and copper-smelting entrepreneurs. Mackworth was a great innovator and in the late seventeenth century he built a short canal and an 'artificial Waggonway on Wooden rails ... for the convenient and cheap Carriage of all Commodities to and fro, from the Canal to the Workhouse, and from the Workhouse to the Canal'.

Iron Forge between Barmouth and Dolgellau
by Paul Sandby, 1776

By permission of the National Library of Wales

'Thy fam'd inventions, Mackworth most
    adorn
The Miner's Art, and make the best Return:
Thy speedy sails, and useful Engines show,
A Genius richer than thy Mines below,
Thousands of Slaves unskill'd Peru
    maintains,
The Hands that labour still exhaust the
    gains:
The Winds thy Slaves, their useful Succours
    joyn,
Convey thy Oar (ore), and labour at thy Mine;
Instructed by thy Art a Power they find
To vanquish Realms, where once they lay
    confin'd.'

Poem by The Reverend Thomas Yalden on the mines of Sir Carberry Price, and dedicated to Sir Humphrey Mackworth.

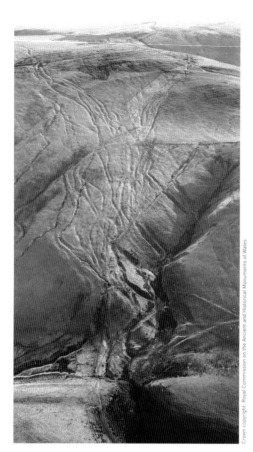

Far left: *Trackways at Mynydd Cil-cwm, west of Newtown. As each trackway became too difficult to use, another was created*

Left: *Drovers in the nineteenth century*

Crown copyright: Royal Commission on the Ancient and Historical Monuments of Wales

Over land

In the eighteenth and first half of the nineteenth centuries, travel could be hazardous: roads were poorly maintained, difficult to negotiate and, in bad weather, sometimes impassable. Journeys crossing rivers and estuaries were lengthy and dangerous.

Carriage of iron products from the ironworks along the northern edge of the south Wales coalfield to the coast needed teams of packhorses linked together in lines, each horse carrying a payload of about 59kg (130lb). In bad weather, the twenty-mile journey from Merthyr Tydfil to Cardiff could take over three days.

The country was crossed by drove roads, along which large numbers of cattle were driven to markets in England. Cattle moved slowly across the country, feeding and fattening as they went; some were so thin at the beginning of their walk that they were described as 'razor-backed mongrels'. The drovers were important to remote rural communities, not only because they were responsible for delivering and selling the cattle, and undertaking the financial transactions, but also because they brought news from the wider world.

LAND

'Gold cannot gold appear, until man's toil
Discloses wide the mountain's hidden ribs
And digs the dusky ore, and breaks and grinds
Its gritty parts.'

The Fleece, John Dyer, 1757

The Iron Age sacrificial offerings found at Llyn Cerrig Bach on Anglesey

The natural wealth of Wales has been exploited for thousands of years, and minerals have always held a special place in human consciousness. One of the main adits at the Dolaucothi Gold Mines at Pumsaint, Carmarthenshire, bears the impression of thousands of small pick marks, which may date from the Roman occupation. Such was their importance that items made from bronze and iron were offered as sacrifices during the Iron Age at Llyn Cerrig Bach on Anglesey. The items included shield fragments, bits from a cauldron and a slave chain, and are now in the National Museum's collections.

Iron, lead, copper, zinc, silver, gold and manganese have been mined at various

A reconstruction of the Iron Age sacrifice at Llyn Cerrig Bach

locations across Wales. Such was the intensity of activity in the nineteenth century that gold-mining near Dolgellau earned it the title of the 'Dolgelly Gold Belt'. One of the most productive mines was Gwynfynydd, where the gold was so valuable that the mine company appointed constables to ensure its safe passage. Lead and zinc were worked extensively in mid- and north-east Wales, and it has been estimated that in the late nineteenth century the value of ore on one estate alone was £4 million.

Wales is also rich in stone quarries. Stone is one of the most versatile materials, and each quarry has its own particular virtues. Blue

Making Setts, by M. E. Thompson, 1949

Lias limestone at Aberthaw provided raw material for the manufacture of cement used in the construction of the Eddystone Lighthouse in the 1820s. Penmaenmawr Quarry was also a good source of granite for the manufacture of curling stones, because of its strength and ability to withstand impact.

Before the widespread use of tarmacadam, urban streets were paved with stone 'setts', square blocks of granite, limestone and sandstone fixed in position with mortar. The quarries at Penmaenmawr were also particularly noted for the quality of their setts. Each block was handmade, and was hammered into shape while held in position by the workman's foot. A lifetime working in this stooped position resulted in some of the older men being described as '*y ddau ben yn dod ynghyd*' (the head and feet coming together).

Penmaenmawr Granite Quarry, Gwynedd c.1906

13

Over water

Bridges were few and far between. Most were made from timber, and it was not uncommon for them to be damaged or even washed away by floods. There were a few exceptions, such as the three-arched Pont Fawr built at Llanrwst in 1636. Its paved surface must have been a brief respite for travellers – the road from there to Llanberis was described as 'the Devil's Bowling Green'.

The large and elegant single arch of stone that spanned the river at Pontypridd caught the imagination of travellers and visitors. Completed by local mason William Edwards in 1755, after three attempts, it was compared by The Reverend Benjamin Malkin in 1804 to the Rialto in Venice:

'The appearance of the bridge from the Llantrisant road has been likened to that of a rainbow: from the lightness, width and elevation of the arc ... It is a question therefore to be asked, what eminent artist, whether from our own or some foreign academy, furnished this extraordinary design.'

Bulk transportation by sea and navigable river operated between the main ports at Carmarthen, Tenby, Cardigan, Aberystwyth and Caernarfon. There were also many other smaller harbours or landing places where boats could be brought in at high tide and loaded or unloaded at low tide.

Pont Fawr bridge in Llanrwst, built in 1636

SEA

Highly polished and, in their time, technologically advanced, the stone axes produced at the prehistoric Penmaenmawr 'Axe factory' and discovered in western England and Northern Ireland are one of the earliest examples of sea trade. The sea has been crucial to the cultural and economic life of Wales. Our ports, harbours, beaches and coves have sent and received goods and people to and from locations around the world.

Slate from Porthmadog, coal from Cardiff and Barry, steel from Newport, tinplate from Swansea, stone from Porthgain and aeroplane wings from Mostyn Dock are just a few examples of the products and places that are part of the story of the sea.

The ports and harbours of Wales reflect the industries and areas they served. A small,

Pembroke Dockyard. The docks are built on a grid iron pattern developed around the naval dockyard established in the nineteenth century

narrow 'cove between two steep rocks where a vessel hath not room to wind, even at high water' became the major copper-exporting port for the great Mynydd Parys mines. Amlwch developed in the eighteenth century to become one of the busiest ports in north Wales, from which large quantities of copper ore were shipped to Swansea. Within a very limited area were copper-smelters, chemical works, warehouses, tobacco works, shipyards and a dry dock.

Milford Haven – mentioned by Shakespeare, and much praised by Lord Nelson – has been the centre of intense maritime activity. The ria, or flooded valley, extends about 30km (18.6 miles) inland and is fed by a series of navigable tributaries. The history of the area offers a potted history of maritime Wales. Milford Haven began life as a Royal Dockyard and then developed as a major fishing port, before becoming the focus for traffic related to the oil refineries. Pembroke Dock took over from Milford Haven as the Royal Dockyard and expanded during the nineteenth century.

A View of Amlwch by Keith Shone. The port at Amlwch served the huge copper mines on Mynydd Parys

People's lives

Workers' homes

Perhaps it is the workers' homes themselves that can tell us most about the lives of our ancestors. As more people came seeking work, more houses were needed. Terraces were built and, more often than not, a maximum number of people were crammed into a minimum amount of space.

Sometimes industrialists built houses for their workers, usually close to their employment. The row of cottages at Cwmafon, north of Pontypool, was built for workers in the local forge in about 1806. Also, there were attempts to create 'model' towns and villages with, in some instances, accommodation being provided for specific groups. The model settlement at Tan-y-Bwlch in Mynydd Llandegai, near Bethesda, was built for workers in Penrhyn Quarry, each house having its own plot of land to encourage self-sufficiency.

'The Ranks' in Abercarn in the 1970s, before bathrooms were installed in the houses

Conditions could be dreadful, especially in the barracks for metal miners and quarry workers. The barracks at the Rhosydd Slate Quarry were described in an *englyn* by Ioan Frothen in the 1920s:

*'Hunaf, a blin yw hynny – yn fy oer
Annifyr lety
A clywaf brath ambell bry
Ar waelod y budr wely'*

'Sleeping, tired out, in my cold
And miserable digs
Feeling the bite of many a bug
At the foot of my filthy bed'

Health

Life in the iron towns was tough, and it could also be short. The average life expectancy for a working person in Merthyr Tydfil in the 1840s was between seventeen and twenty years. The high death rates among children under the age of five at this time partly account for this appalling statistic; if you lived through the first few years of existence in the town, your chances of survival improved. Unless, that is, you were unlucky enough to be living in the town during a visitation of cholera. In 1839, over 1,400 people died of this disease in Merthyr Tydfil, and such was the anxiety felt by the population that many temporarily fled the town.

The Unknown Female Worker

We don't know her name, her exact place of birth, where precisely she worked or how and when she died. She represents the thousands of unknown and unsung heroes who worked and lived in industrial Wales. Without their efforts over the past 300 years, our lives today would be so much poorer. She was photographed by William Clayton in his studio in Tredegar about 1860. Carrying her food box and water can, she has just finished, or is about to start, her shift in one of the local ironstone mines. Even though her work was arduous, her hat is decorated and she wears a scarf or some kind of ruff around her neck. Judging by the fall of her skirt, she may even have been several months' pregnant at the time.

Many urban problems were caused by a lack of clean water and by inadequate sewage disposal. An eyewitness account of Merthyr in 1853 makes grim reading:

'I can hardly expect credence for such facts as the following yet it is perfectly free from exaggeration. I saw a young woman filling her pitcher from a little stream of water gushing from a cinder heap the surface of which was so thickly studded with alvine deposits that it was difficult to pass without treading on them, in some of which I saw intestinal worms, and the rain then falling was washing the feculent matter into the water which the girl was filling into her pitcher, no doubt for domestic use.'

Little wonder then that a national solution to these problems emerged from Wales, where Aneurin Bevan used the Medical Aid Society in Tredegar as the basis for his National Health Service in 1948.

A woman's work

Women played an essential part in the making of industrial Wales and, during the nineteenth century, were employed in mines and ironworks. Usually they were engaged to fill trucks and barrows, pick coal from screens, break iron ore or limestone or carry out many other 'manual' tasks. Although they worked alongside men doing exactly the same work in many instances, they were often paid at lower rates. And, of course, in addition to their paid work, women were also responsible for running the household and bringing up their families.

The presence of women in the workplace generated a great deal of interest from visitors and social reformers. Arthur Mumby visited Blaenafon in 1865 and noted:

'The Welshman named Powell showed me around .... Some women were filling and wheeling barrows of ironstone: but most were engaged inside certain wooden sheds in breaking the big lumps of ironstone .... Lifting the hammer over their heads and bringing it down with manly skill and force .... They were well grown lasses from 15 to 21 .... Mr Powell said, "they are the finest women of this kind anywhere, and if it wasn't for the girls here I don't know what the ironworks would do."'

ACHIEVERS:
Aneurin Bevan

More commonly known as 'Nye' Bevan, he was born in Tredegar in 1897. Growing up during a period of political and cultural change, he became deeply involved in the labour struggle and the development of the labour movement. He was renowned for his oratory skills and entered Parliament in 1929. He said, 'I never used to regard myself so much as a politician as a projectile discharged from the Welsh valleys'. He will long be remembered as the principal architect of the National Health Service – the nationalisation of medicine and treatment. It can be argued that its introduction has been one of the most significant pieces of legislation ever passed.

Aneurin, or 'Nye'
Bevan, in 1945

MONEY

Cwmbach Co-operative Society shop, *c*.1910

Cash was not always readily available in the early nineteenth century, as many workers were paid in tokens or company money that could be redeemed only at company shops, where prices could be inflated and the quality of goods on offer was variable.

Because of the lack of coinage in the system, the Parys Mine Company began to issue its own copper tokens in 1787. These were considered to be exceptionally good value for their design, production and high content of copper, but unfortunately many counterfeit copies were made and they were declared illegal in 1817.

In the iron and coal industries there could be long periods between pay days. As late as the 1890s, coal miners were paid fortnightly, and the alternate Saturdays with and without pay were known as *Sadwrn talu* ('Pay Saturday') and *Sadwrn du* ('Black Saturday'). Cash flow was a problem that was often resolved only by recourse to the pawnbroker or loan shark, and low wages or wage cuts led to strikes and confrontations.

Local shopkeepers often had to operate on a great deal of trust, and during strikes or lockouts many provided food and goods to needy families on 'tick', or on the 'slate' or 'tab'. Supplying a wide range of goods, local stores occupied an important place in the community. The Gwalia Stores in St Fagans National History Museum is a typical example, with a grocery section and, in its original setting, an extensive range of ironmongery.

The local Co-op store was a blessing to many industrial communities. Operating on a membership basis, and paying dividends (the 'divi') on purchases, these stores provided the basis for earnings to be accumulated.

Department stores opened in larger towns. Among some of the best known were James Howells and David Morgan in Cardiff, and David Evans and Lewis Lewis's in Swansea.

19

Riots against wage cuts
by Penry Williams, 1816–17

© Cyfarthfa Castle Museum and Art Gallery, Merthyr Tydfil

Uprising and unrest

Worker unrest was a cause for concern for some of the ironmasters. At Nantyglo are the remains of fortified fireproof towers, built in 1816 to provide temporary protection for the ironmaster and his family in case of a workers' uprising. The iron door has twin musket apertures, set at knee and hip level, to repel potential attacks.

A series of bloody confrontations occurred in the first half of the nineteenth century along the iron belt of south Wales. The red flag, which became a worldwide symbol for worker solidarity, is reputed to have been raised for the first time at Hirwaun during 1831. Thousands of workers in Merthyr Tydfil rose in support of the Reform Bill and in defiance of wage cuts and the Court of Requests. In the ensuing confrontation with troops, twenty-four workers were killed, seventy were wounded and the troops were expelled from the town. The workers held out for four days, but were ultimately crushed by superior force and armaments.

One twenty-three-year-old miner, Richard Lewis (famously known as 'Dic Penderyn'), was wrongly convicted of wounding a soldier in the attack and was hanged on the gallows in St Mary's Street, Cardiff. His last words on the scaffold were, '*O Arglwydd, dyma gamwedd*' ('O Lord, this is injustice'). A plaque now marks the spot.

Religion

Religion was important in the mining communities; indeed, Nonconformity dominated industrial Wales. Such was the power of the movement that by 1851 it was recorded in the Census that seven out of ten places of worship in Wales were Nonconformist. The industrial streets of Wales were punctuated by the 'palaces of the Oral Arts', as the chapels were known. The 1856 Rule Book for the Taff Vale Railway recommended that every employee should 'attend a place of worship, as it will be a means of promotion when vacancies occur'. Many chapels are very similar in appearance to the engine houses of the local collieries, as they were often built by the same craftsmen.

The powerful combination of Nonconformity and Liberalism was influential in forming the society of industrial Wales to such an extent that in 1891 W. E. Gladstone declared that 'the Nonconformists are the people of Wales'.

The chapels exerted great influence on society. They were in the forefront of the Temperance Movement that resulted in the Sunday Closing Act of 1881, bringing about the closure of all public houses in Wales on a Sunday.

Chapels were more than places of religion, they were often the focus of many social activities as well. The Whit Sunday walk was an important event when various congregations would parade through the streets.

Far left: *Capel y Tabernacl in Llanelli*

Above: *The Whitsun Chapel Walk at Salem Chapel in Pantygog in the Garw Valley, c.1908*

PEOPLE

By the mid-nineteenth century, the people of Wales were beginning to understand the effects of industrialisation. The 1851 Census returns for Wales show that, for the first time in any country, more people were working in industry than in agriculture – in a land where the many found employment in industries that were owned by the few. Wales can therefore claim to be the world's first industrial nation, an assertion supported by the numerous other world-firsts in technology and engineering.

Railways had made movement much easier and there was a coming together of town and country. Industrial Wales was Welsh-speaking and, although immigrants were arriving daily from England and Ireland, it was not until the end of the century that Anglicisation began to take effect.

Nonconformity was the main religion, and it has been estimated that a new chapel was being opened every eight days at this time.

Wales was changing rapidly, and it is from this time onwards that many of the commonly held stereotypes have emerged – male-voice choirs, tip-scarred valleys, the Welsh 'Mam', a reputation for militancy and a great sense of solidarity and community.

Differences between the rich and the poor were vast. The richest landowners owned estates where industry was flourishing – the Marquis of Bute in Glamorgan, Lord Tredegar in Monmouthshire and the Penrhyn family in Bethesda all lived in palatial mansions. At the opposite end of the scale were those who lived and worked in some of the worst conditions imaginable. A report of 1849 on public health in Swansea noted a house in Mariner Street where one of the privies was:

'inundated by the liquid contents of the pit ... too filthy to be entered. The residents buy most of their drinking water at this time of year, as they can rarely get any at Dyfatty spout without waiting for hours'.

Coal Staithe on River Tawe by J. C. Ibbetson, 1792

COMMUNITIES

A coach and horses outing from Butetown in Cardiff, early twentieth century

Wales may speak with one voice when cheering on the national side at the Millennium Stadium, but the country is composed of a series of groups and settlements, each with its own individual character and history. The people of industrial Wales come from a rich and diverse background – a mixture of Welsh, English, Irish and Scots with a sprinkling of Italian and Spanish for good measure.

A quarrying settlement in Gwynedd was both similar to, and different from, an iron town in Monmouthshire or a coal-mining valley in Glamorgan. The three places each depended on a single monolithic industry, which generated relatively high wages when times were good but could experience severe hardship when times were bad.

The main difference lay in the nature of their respective societies. The quarrying community was predominantly Welsh-speaking and originated from a fairly localised catchment area. The towns in south Wales, particularly Cardiff, comprised a mix of peoples – some Welsh-speaking – who were drawn from rural Wales, England, Ireland and elsewhere.

In his epic poem The Angry Summer, Idris Davies wrote about '... the little Italian shop – where they sell coloured gassy pop'. The Italian ice-cream shop s had a great impact on life in the industrial communities; warm and welcoming, they provided much-needed meeting places. Many of the families that ran them came from Bardi in northern Italy. The first shops to open were owned by the Bracchi family and, for a time, were known simply as 'Bracchi's'. Italians also worked in the tinplate industry in south-west Wales immediately after the Second World War.

Cardiff's rise as the main coal-exporting port attracted workers from all over the world. The docks area is one of the most multicultural ports in Britain, with people from the Caribbean, Asia, Somalia, Yemen and more besides. It has been estimated that, in the 1940s, there were about fifty nations represented in a population of about 5,000.

There was a Jewish community in Swansea in the 1730s, and the communities spread into the rest of industrial south Wales in the nineteenth century, particularly around Cardiff and Merthyr Tydfil, which had a synagogue and a Jewish cemetery. Anti-Jewish attacks in the early decades of the twentieth century led to a decline in the Jewish population. In 1913, it was estimated there were about 5,000 Jewish people in Wales; the 2001 census showed there were about 2,000.

ORGANISATIONS

The Reading Room in Oakdale Workingmen's Institute, *c.*1946. The Institute has been re-erected, brick by brick, at St Fagans National History Museum

Underpinning the industrialisation of Wales was a network of interlocking and interdependent organisations. The wide range of these organisations reflected the richness and variety of the societies they served.

Unionism has been a powerful force throughout modern history, with its roots in the struggle to improve conditions and resist exploitation. One of the most influential and powerful unions was the South Wales Miners' Federation, which was formed in 1898 and fought long and bitterly on behalf of miners and their communities. In the slate industry, the North Wales Quarryman's Union fought equally hard for its members and was at the forefront of the dispute that resulted in the Penrhyn Quarry Lockout of 1901–3 – the longest in British labour history.

Sennybridge football team, 1910

Many communities raised funds to build and sustain Working Men's Institutes. These were very important cultural centres, with theatres, billiard and snooker rooms, libraries, reading rooms and educational facilities.

The Royal Institution of South Wales – now the Swansea Museum – was opened in 1841 for the 'advancement of Science, Literature and the Arts'. Chapels performed a similar role, in that their cultural and educational activities extended beyond their religious function.

There were organisations for sport, literature and music, Friendly Societies and debating groups. On or near the full moon every month, *Y Gymdeithas Loerig* (The Lunar Society) met in Dolgellau to discuss literary and scientific matters. The Lunar Society was founded in Birmingham and had branches across Britain; during the late eighteenth century it was considered nearly as prestigious as the Royal Society.

The Women's Suffrage Movement fought passionately for votes for women, and the National Union of Women's Suffrage Society had branches across Wales. The campaign for votes for women began in the 1860s, and full suffrage was finally achieved in 1938.

ACHIEVERS:
Gareth Edwards

Given the significance of rugby in the cultural life of Wales, and the particular importance of the game to the industrial communities, Gareth Edwards must rank as one of our favourite heroes. Born in 1947 in Gwauncaegurwen, he excelled in the sport at school. He gained his first cap for Wales aged nineteen, and by the following year he was captain of the team. A superb athlete and excellent sportsman, he played for Wales on fifty-three consecutive occasions and scored twenty tries for his country. His remarkable try for the Barbarians against the All Blacks in 1973 has an unshakeable place in Welsh rugby and cultural history. From his key position as scrum half, he guided Wales to three Grand Slams and five Triple Crowns.

Gareth Edwards playing for the British Lions in 1974

© Western Mail and Echo Ltd

Industries

Metals

By the late eighteenth century, Bersham in north Wales had become an important centre for iron manufacture, built around the skills and inventiveness of John Wilkinson. He was nicknamed 'Iron Mad' because he is reputed never to have written a letter without mentioning the word 'iron' at least once. His ironworks became famous for the production of cannon and steam-engine cylinders, produced to a high specification by his water-powered boring machine. For over twenty years, he supplied cylinders to Boulton and Watt, the great steam-engine manufacturers.

Chirk Castle gates, made by the Davies brothers of Croesfoel and reproduced here on a postcard in 1909

Near to Bersham was the early eighteenth-century ironwork forge of the Davies brothers – Robert and John – of Croesfoel. They were highly skilled craftsmen, and their gates at Chirk are among the best examples of ornamental ironwork in Europe.

The Swansea valley was opened up in 1798 by the completion of the Swansea Canal and by the tram roads that linked industries to the canal. Swansea was the largest town in Wales in 1800, with a population of 6,831, dependent upon metal-smelting and manufacture. But Merthyr Tydfil was rapidly catching up and would soon overtake Swansea as the largest industrial town in Wales, and Wrexham in north-east Wales was also growing rapidly, based around iron manufacture and coal mining.

The former Cistercian Abbey at Neath was once used to accommodate workers, as it was situated alongside both the coal mines and the copper works. The Neath Abbey Ironworks produced some of the highest-quality engineering products. It was one of the most important ironworks in Wales, manufacturing beam engines, railway locomotives, ships and smaller engines.

Around the start of the nineteenth century, dramatic changes were taking place in Wales. Along the Heads of the Valleys of south Wales, ironworks and towns were expanding at an

26

Neath Abbey *by Edward Donovan, 1805*

astonishing rate. Merthyr Tydfil, Tredegar, Ebbw Vale and Blaenafon were becoming world-famous for the manufacture of pig iron and bar iron, and thousands of people flocked there in search of work.

By the end of the nineteenth century, the iron and steel works along the Heads of the Valleys were in decline, and new works were built along the coast to take advantage of iron ore imported from overseas.

An exception were the works at Ebbw Vale, where substantial investment resulted in the rebuilding of the works in the 1930s and the opening of the hot-strip mill for the manufacture of tinplate and sheet steel for the car industry.

Tinplate had been produced on a large scale in south-west Wales by the old hand-mill process, with Llanelli nicknamed 'Tinopolis' because of the number of works in the locality. The old mills were ultimately replaced by the huge strip mills at Trostre,

Llanelli, Velindre, north of Swansea and Ebbw Vale. Velindre closed in 1989 and all traces of the works have been removed.

Massive works were built at Port Talbot and Llanwern after the Second World War, including the construction of the huge deep-water ore terminal at Port Talbot. The works have provided employment for thousands of people, and they are now among the most modern in Europe.

The tools for the job – hammers and drills

Until the advent of mechanical drills and the use of explosives, technology changed little in the metal mines of Wales. The basic tools were hammers and picks. At the Great Orme Copper Mines, near Llandudno, literally thousands of broken pieces of antler have been discovered, which were used as picks during the Bronze Age to dislodge the ore-bearing rock that had first been loosened using stone hammers.

27

Metal mining and separation of the useable ore from the worthless rock is a process of continual reduction. At the great copper mines on Mynydd Parys in Anglesey in the eighteenth century, this was a job for women – the *Copar Ladis* ('Copper Ladies') – and young children. They used hammers to pound the rock on anvils, known locally as 'knockers', protecting their hands with strong leather gloves sheathed in metal plates.

Parys Mountain, Copar Ladis *by J. C. Ibbetson, 1795*

Tinplate manufacturing

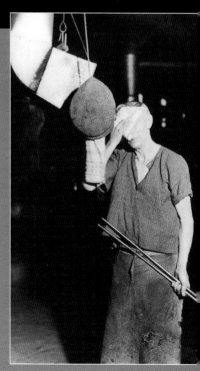

At the end of the nineteenth century, south-west Wales became a major centre for the manufacture of tinplate, particularly at Llanelli, which was nicknamed 'Tinopolis'.

From the moment a steel bar arrived in the works, it was heated and reheated, rolled and rerolled, squeezed, sheared, cleaned with acid, covered with molten tin and polished until it had been transformed into a sheet of shiny tinplate ready for quality-checking and dispatch.

The Rollerman was responsible for passing the plates through the rolls and 'screwing down' the gap between the rolls. The Doubler, as the name suggests, 'folded' the sheets. The Behinder returned the plates over the top of the mill to the Rollerman, and then the First and Second Helpers provided additional support.

The hot plates were gripped and moved using a variety of tongs. This was work that was exhausting and potentially dangerous, as the plates were quite literally flung across the floor during the process. A visitor to one of the works described it as 'a lot of madmen throwing hot plates at each other'.

Women worked in the tinplate industry, separating and cleaning the plates. This too was arduous work, requiring skill and experience. They used separators to open up the plates that had stuck together. These were blocks of lead fixed to leather 'palms', which were struck against the plates to break them apart. If the plates were firmly stuck together a broad-bladed, sword-like implement called a hanger was used to separate them.

TRANSFORMATIONS

From iron ore to railway line, from a lump of galena to a water pipe, from a piece of copper ore to the windings of an electric motor, from a small lump of gold to the circuit in a computer – all these transformations require a complex and highly skilled technological process.

It has been the transformation of raw materials on a large scale into a myriad of different uses that epitomises the past 200 years and more – a period when the manufacture of metals became less of an art and more of a science.

Modern life depends on the efficient production and distribution of power, and this is only possible through the use of a huge number of metal-based products. The transformation, for example, of a chunk of ironstone mined in south Wales to become part of a rail laid in Siberia or North America involved a complex technological process and a rich human story.

A 'puddler' at work

Mynydd Parys

Parys Mine, engraving by J. Bluck, 1795, based on a painting by J. C. Ibbetson

Massive deposits of copper ore had been worked at the old Mynydd Parys mines on Anglesey since the mid-seventeenth century, creating one of the most extraordinary industrial landscapes in Europe. For over 250 years Mynydd Parys, as it is now known, has attracted visitors, many of whom have been astonished by what they see.

The Reverend George Bingley, who visited in 1799, wrote:

'Having … ascended to the top, I found myself standing on the verge of a vast and tremendous chasm. I stepped on one of the stages, suspended over the edge of the steep, and the prospect was dreadful: The number of caverns at different heights along the sides; the broken and irregular masses of rock … the multitudes of men at work … the motions of the whimsies, and the raising and lowering of the buckets, to draw out the ore and the rubbish: the noise of picking the ore from the rock …: the roar of the blasts in distant parts, of the mine, altogether excited the most sublime ideas, intermixed, however, with sensations of terror.'

At the time, the Mynydd Parys mines were the largest producers of copper ore in the world.

Parys Mine, Anglesey, by William Havell. *c.*1803

METALS

The conversion of metal ores into useable products lay at the heart of the industrial revolution. The manufacture of products made from iron, steel and tinplate and the use of copper, lead and other non-ferrous metals in the workplace and home have changed the way we live.

The cast iron Waterloo Bridge in Betws y Coed

At times, Wales has led the world in technological achievements, from the first production of rolled tinplate sheet in Pontypool by John Hanbury in the seventeenth and early eighteenth centuries, to the

pioneering work carried out at the Hafod Copper Works in Swansea in the nineteenth century, and the production of nickel at the Mond Works in Clydach in the twentieth century. These are just a few of the innovations that exemplified Wales.

Large metal containers being made in Swansea, early twentieth century

31

Fact and fiction intermingle at Pumsaint near the Dolaucothi Mines, where a large stone block used as an anvil for separating gold from rock became associated with the legend of the five saints who, while on a pilgrimage to St David's, are said to have rested their heads on the stone during a hailstorm. The velocity and size of the hailstones pounded their heads with such force as to leave indentations on the rock surface. The marks were in fact formed by the constant pounding of hand-held or mechanical hammers.

The tools for the job – shears and tongs

The manufacture of iron and steel, tinplate and copper underpinned the industrial economy of Wales for many years. Fundamental to the success of those industries were the skills of their workforces.

Right: The 'Five Saints' stone at Pumsaint

Below: Tredegar Ironworks, 1912

WORKING THE ROLLS AT TREDEGAR IRON WORKS. 287.

Until the great improvements in safety precautions in the second half of the twentieth century, these industries could be dangerous environments. Shears and tongs were designed to minimise the proximity of hot metal, yet at the same time ensure that the hot metals could be handled relatively easily.

To produce bar iron required the passage of red-hot bars through a series of fast-moving rollers. As they passed through the rolls, the bars were squeezed and elongated. After each 'pass', they were manually turned and passed back over the rolls for the next 'pass'. This work required great strength, skill and dexterity.

Another skilled process involved forging metal under the stroke of a mechanical hammer. With the use of tongs and bars, the hot metal was constantly moved until it was worked into the required shape and consistency. This process was also used to manufacture a range of tools, and across Wales there were many foundries producing goods for local markets. The Aberaeron tilt hammer (on display in the Museum) was used to make sickles and shovels. It was powered by a waterwheel and could operate at about 140 beats per minute.

'A bar of iron, as it passes through each successive groove of a pair of rolls, is received on the opposite side by two men, one of whom draws it out by the end with a pair of tongs, and the other supports it by a level, to prevent its making too sudden a bend; and when the bar is through, these men pitch it back again over the top roll for it to pass through the next groove, and this operation is repeated until the bar is reduced to the required size .... The spectator, who may have taken his stand at a convenient distance, and has scarcely been able to comprehend more than the possibility of what he has seen done, from the celerity of its execution, is probably obliged to move farther off by the scorching heat of the still bright-red, long, finished bar which has reached him.'

Guide to Merthyr Tydfil, 1894

32

Billet rolling at Panteg Steelworks in 1966

33

The great Dinorwig Slate Quarry, Llanberis, in 1949. The scale of the workings, the huge tips of waste and the incline systems illustrate the skill and ingenuity required to produce slate

Slate

Wales was a world-centre of slate production. Huge quarries and mines were opened and, as more railways were constructed and demand increased for this high-quality, durable roofing material, so the landscape changed. Quarries and mines increased in size, and large waste tips of both slate and rock spread out from them. Quarry faces and dressing sheds were linked by inclines and hoists, in a demonstration of marvellous engineering.

Inevitably, it was around the mines and quarries that communities grew up. Places such as Blaenau Ffestiniog, Bethesda, Llanberis and Nantlle evolved as industrial settlements, with concentrations of terraced houses, shops, chapels and public houses. The settlements grew in a haphazard manner as the quarries expanded, and today there is still no mistaking the significance that slate played in the history of these localities. Blaenau Ffestiniog, although long past its heyday as a quarrying town, still produces slate – indeed, slate from this area has been used in the construction of the National Waterfront Museum. And in Llanberis, dominated by the massive

Dinorwig Quarries that operated for over 200 years until their closure in 1969, the former workshops have been preserved as the National Slate Museum, which vividly illustrates the rich cultural and technical story of slate.

The language of the slate quarries has always been Welsh, as the people drawn into the quarrying communities in the nineteenth century came mainly from the surrounding parishes.

The slate communities were close-knit, particularly at times of conflict, although during the great strike of 1900–3 at Penrhyn Quarry, the hardship was such that some men returned to work – thereafter becoming known as *Bradwyr* ('Traitors').

The life of the quarry owner was far removed from that of the quarry workers and their families. The owners of Penrhyn Quarry, for example, lived in Penrhyn Castle nearby (now in the care of the National Trust), and the Penrhyn estates once covered about 72,000 acres.

Transportation of slate to the ports was crucial. Early methods used carts and

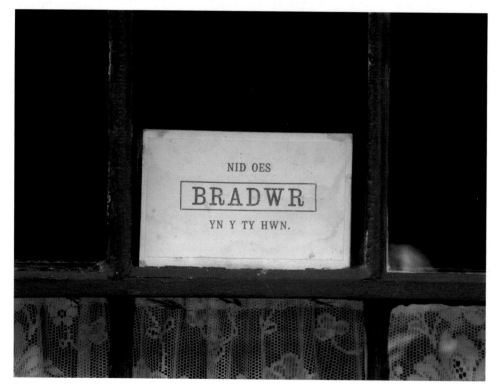

The sign reads 'There is no Traitor in this house', referring to the fifty-five workers who went back to work at Penrhyn Slate Quarry in November 1901. The strike went on to be the longest in British industrial history

*The stack yard at Llechwedd
Slate Quarry, c.1895*

Gwynedd Archives Service

sledges along poor roads or small boats
along navigable waterways. Slate was loaded
onto lighters at the quays on the Afon Glaslyn
near Maentwrog, and then transported to
Porthmadog on the coast. The boatmen who
transported the slate were nicknamed 'the
Philistines', because of their opposition to
the Ffestiniog Railway. Their opposition is
understandable, as the railways replaced
boats as a means of transporting the slate.

Narrow-gauge railways were also vital
for efficient transportation, linking remote
inland quarries to the coast and negotiating
routes through the mountainous landscape.
They are a testament to the remarkable

skills of the engineers and builders of the
day. Wherever possible, the railways
followed the land's natural contours, but
many quarries were accessible only via
inclines. Wales has some of the most
spectacular examples of narrow-gauge
railways, in terms of their engineering and
location. The Rhosydd Quarry incline at the
head of Cwm Croesor is one of the most
impressive, as it drops precipitously to link
with a narrow-gauge railway to Porthmadog,
the busiest slate-exporting port in north-
west Wales. The Ffestiniog Railway was
opened in 1836 to link Porthmadog with
Blaenau Ffestiniog.

Porthmadog

The port town of Porthmadog was named after William Maddocks, who was responsible for the construction of The Cob – part of a massive land-reclamation scheme in the Glaslyn Estuary. The diverted river scoured out the approach to the harbour, allowing access for ocean-going ships.

The town and port developed as a shipbuilding centre in the nineteenth century; the ships created there were among the best of their kind. Aled Eames, an expert on the maritime history of the area, described them as 'quite outstanding vessels, the ultimate development of small wooden merchant sailing ships in Britain'.

Slate from Porthmadog was transported across the world, and the town had shipbrokers, a School of Navigation, sail lofts, rope-walks and its own Maritime Insurance Office.

Gwynedd Archives Service

Porthmadog harbour, 1890

By permission of the National Library of Wales

The Embankment, Traeth Mawr, Tremadoc by H. Billington, 1810, showing The Cob under construction

37

Right: *A quarry worker using a 'jumper' to drill a hole in the slate*

Below: *Quarry workers 'dressing' slate in Penrhyn Quarry*

The tools for the job – chisels and knives

Hammers, wedges, chisels, bars and gougers were used in slate quarrying. Black powder was used to blast large slabs of rock away from the face. The shot holes were drilled by using a long chisel-ended bar, called a 'jumper'. Drilling one hole could take up to a day.

The blocks were broken down using a hammer and chisel; sometimes a huge hammer called a *Rhys Mawr* was used. When broken into manageable thicknesses, they were split into the fine sheets using a broad-bladed chisel called a 'manhollt' and a hammer made of African oak. The workman, with his legs crossed at his ankles, sat on a high-backed low stool for this work.

Once split, the sheets were passed to another member of the team who cut the slate to size. He sat on a sloping bench, known as a trafal, and trimmed the slate to size against a fixed metal edge. The sizes were measured using a notched measuring stick, and cut using a large knife (*cylleth fawr*).

Although parts of the slate production process were mechanised, the splitting (or 'dressing') of slate is still done by hand – a skill that requires immense experience and knowledge.

The National Wool Museum in west Wales, in an area once known as 'The Huddersfield of Wales'

© Paul Avis

Textiles

Until the nineteenth century, the most widespread and important industry in rural Wales was textile manufacturing. In nearly every locality spinners, carders, weavers and fullers could be found. A wide range of cloths was produced, from hard-wearing coarse fabric to finer decorative materials. Starting as a home-based industry – many houses had their own spinning wheel – weaving gradually became more formalised and mechanised.

With the introduction of larger hand looms, new buildings were required. In Llanidloes and Newtown were three- and four-storey buildings with living accommodation below and looms on the upper floors. Large windows featured prominently, as natural light was important.

The arrival of the Shropshire Canal in Newtown in 1821 increased the potential for trade. The resulting concentration of textile production in large factories was so great that the town was nicknamed 'The Leeds of Wales'. In 1837, there were seventy-four weaving factories in Newtown alone. Women formed a high percentage of the workforce, especially in work requiring great dexterity.

The Teifi Valley in south-west Wales evolved as an important centre of production, with water-powered factories built close to the streams and rivers. By the end of the nineteenth century, more than fifty mills were in operation there. Among their main products were flannel shirts, which were worn in the mining, steel and tinplate industries because they were hard-wearing and absorbed sweat.

The National Wool Museum at Dre-fach Felindre, near Llandysul, tells the story of manufacturing at a time when that area was known as 'The Huddersfield of Wales'.

Greenfield Valley

A mini industrial revolution took place in the narrow Greenfield Valley, near Holywell, with its textile mills, copper works and brewing. The valley is a microcosm of the diverse industrialisation of wider north-east Wales. From the mid-eighteenth century, the huge quantities of water that supplied St Winifred's Well were utilised to power a variety of industries: copper works were in production in 1755, supplied with ingots from Parys Mountain, and battery works produced brass pots and pans. Other works in the valley produced small, shiny copper articles – jewellery and mirrors for example – as currency for the slave trade. They also made fine sheets to protect the undersides of ships trading in warm waters from timber-boring worms that could wreak considerable damage.

The vast supplies of water in the area were more than adequate to power the massive textile mills that would not have been out of place in the north-east of England. Thomas Pennant described the valley in 1773 as having 'battering mills for copper, a wire-mill, coarse paper-mill, snuff-mill and a foundry for brass. A cotton manufactory is establishing, the success of which will be an extensive blessing to the neighbourhood'. According to Pennant, the Cotton Twist Company had over 1,225 employees by 1796.

The expansion of coal mining saw the growth of the towns in the locality, especially Wrexham and Ruabon. Complete new villages also appeared in response to the demand from an expanding workforce. The coal mines mainly served the local industries and communities. Rhosllanerchrugog and Bagillt were mining villages that quickly developed their own cultural character and physical identity. The terraced houses are built mainly out of the brick for which north-east Wales became particularly famous, especially the Ruabon Marl, which was mined alongside the coal measures.

© Flintshire Record Office

A textile mill in Greenfield Valley, c.1796

Left: *International Colliery, Blaengarw*

Bottom left: *The Crumlin Viaduct, c.1900*

Coal

From the 1840s onwards, the production of coal for export became increasingly important in the economy. A series of Admiralty trials between 1846 and 1875 had demonstrated the superiority of Welsh steam coal, and the demand for 'smokeless Welsh'

rose sharply as the navies of the world followed the example of the British navy.

The result was a ferocious onslaught on the coal reserves of south Wales in particular. Collieries and levels appeared throughout the sparsely inhabited pastoral valleys of Monmouthshire, Glamorganshire and Carmarthenshire. The pattern of growth within the region was naturally uneven, arising from the complex interaction of a number of geological, technical, transport and economic factors. The overall expansion, however, was massive.

Across south Wales, coal mining dominated the landscape. Intense concentrations of dwellings were compressed between the hills, and long, narrow lines of terraced housing snaked along the floors and lower slopes of the

41

Right: *The Black Eyes jazz band*, 1926

Bottom right: *Abercarn Amateur Operatic Society, 1925*

valleys. Coal was the 'king' of the Welsh economy. In 1913 output peaked when the south Wales coalfield produced nearly fifty-seven million tons of coal. In the anthracite-mining areas development came a little later, and many places were a mixture of industrial and semi-rural environments.

Mining areas were linked by a network of railways to the busy ports facing the Bristol Channel. The first railways followed the alignment of the valleys, but such was the demand for high-quality coal that lines were built across the grain of the land, spanning valleys with great viaducts and piercing the hills with long tunnels.

The mining areas were vibrant places, and the society that populated the narrow valleys came from far and wide. The valleys were also places of fun and enjoyment. Jazz

bands were popular during the 1920s and '30s, theatres and cinemas were invariably full, and choirs and operatic societies often had waiting lists for membership.

Mining was dangerous, and pit accidents were commonplace. The Tynewydd Colliery in Porth, Rhondda, was the scene of a

Rhondda

At the heart of the coalfield was 'Rhondda' – the term generally used to describe the twin valleys of Rhondda Fawr and Rhondda Fach. The name Rhondda was once synonymous with coal mining and, during the late nineteenth century, it was the most important coal-mining area in Britain.

A visitor to the upper reaches of Rhondda Fawr in 1848 described it thus: 'The air is aromatic with wild flowers, and mountain plants – a Sabbath stillness reigns.'

A tram road opened up the lower reaches of the valley in the early nineteenth century, and this was followed by the Taff Vale Railway in the 1850s, which expanded to all parts of the valleys. After the decision by the Admiralty in 1851 to use Welsh steam coal, the expansion was staggering. People flowed into the valleys from far and wide, providing labour for the rapidly expanding industry. Pits were sunk and villages rapidly sprang up around them, comprising snaking terraces of two-storey houses, which both followed and ignored the natural contours.

These terraces were punctuated by chapels, Working Men's Institutes and public houses. The villages merged with each other, producing a sinuous conurbation that runs almost without break from Trehafod in the south to Blaenrhondda and Maerdy in the north.

At its peak, just before the First World War, there were over fifty large collieries and many more small drifts and levels at work. By 1924 some 160,000 people were crammed into the narrow confines. The story of Rhondda is told at the Rhondda Heritage Park, located in and around the buildings of the Lewis Merthyr Colliery, which was closed in 1983.

Most of the tips that once characterised the valleys have been removed and landscaped, after the disaster at Aberfan in 1966, when 116 children and twenty-eight adults died after a colliery waste tip collapsed and demolished the school and neighbouring houses.

Crown copyright: Royal Commission on the Ancient and Historical Monuments of Wales

43

Right: *The survivors of the Tynewydd Colliery disaster*

Bottom right: *Repairing a roof fall underground*

celebrated rescue in 1877 when nine survivors were saved after being trapped by flooding. Five of the survivors had been trapped underground for nine days.

There were times of prosperity in the valleys, and there could be hardship. Mining was sometimes poorly paid, so there was a constant battle to improve conditions and wages. However, strikes were a last resort, as everyone was only too aware of the hardship they could bring.

The tools for the job – pick and shovel

Throughout Wales, the pick and shovel are strongly associated with coal mining; before the mechanisation of the pits, the most important tools used by the collier were his pick (or mandrel) and his shovel. Together they form one of the most formidable combinations of tools known in history. In skilled hands, they have dammed rivers, excavated canals, sunk shafts, dug tunnels, opened railway cuttings and even moved mountains.

A collier would have taken great care of his tools, always locking them together on the bar before leaving work so that they could not be used by anyone else. When a collier said 'put the tools on the bar' it signalled the end of the shift. The words were also sometimes used symbolically to mark the beginning of a strike or lock-out. Bringing tools out of the mine often meant that the stoppage could be prolonged.

COAL

Holeing the coal by candlelight

A collier was not simply a hewer of coal. He had to understand the nature of the seams and ventilation systems; he had to learn how to erect roof supports; he had to know how to use his tools properly and, most importantly, he had to be aware of the constant dangers of working in such an extreme environment.

Working in pairs or small groups, with responsibility for their own small work place and the safety of their work mates, bred a great sense of independence and interdependence. Good colliers were, as a former miner said, 'Kings in their stalls' – yet they were always ready to help their neighbour. The strong sense of community in their working environment continued to the surface, and the mining communities had a reputation for solidarity and unity.

'I was working with my father and brother … we was working three in a place and I was number three. Then I went to work … gathering the small lumps and you had a basket thing, a curling box. You'd carry that to the dram while your butty was getting on with the big lumps. It wasn't long before they'd expect you to be cutting posts.'

James Minton, recalling working in the late nineteenth century in the mines near Blaina.

'Before the days of machine mining in south Wales each collier had his own working place, in much the same way an allotment holder has his own plot. He worked his own plot in his own way without interference from anyone; it was his own little domain … and he had to live on what he could get out of it.'

Edmond Stonelake of Aberdare, about his life in the pits in the early twentieth century.

A 'place' was the particular section of the seam allocated to a miner and his work mates. A 'curling box' was a flat-bottomed scoop used for loading lump coal. 'Drams' were the main method of underground haulage before conveyor belts. The top of the dram was splayed to maximise its carrying capacity, a process known in some areas as 'racing'. The number of the stall was chalked on the front so that the amount of coal could be allocated to the particular miner and his butty after being weighed.

Working with poor flickering lighting could cause a complaint called Nystagmus, which was nicknamed 'The Staggers'. The strain of working with such poor lighting caused muscle weakness in the eyes that could lead to rapid, involuntary eye movement, which in turn sometimes resulted in giddiness or blackouts.

DAY'S WORK

The experience of a day's work in 2005 is very different from that of 1905. There has been a transformation in the type of work available and the skills required by the workforce.

At the beginning of the twentieth century, most people worked in industries where the emphasis was on the production of materials and goods. They were probably engaged in manual labour and might well have worked in environments where there was little consideration for hygiene or safety. There were few facilities available; if they were lucky they might have had a small cabin where they could eat their food. Lavatories and washing facilities were few and far between. They would have lived within easy travelling distance of their place of employment, in a community that was largely reliant on that particular works. Therefore, there would have been a very strong sense of shared experience.

Work is now undertaken by both men and women (in fact, by the turn of the twenty-first century, 51% of the paid workforce are women) who may well live many miles from their place of work and travel daily in their own car. The standard of welfare and work place facilities bears little comparison to that of their forebears. Working hours, rates of pay and health and safety issues are all now covered by legislation.

There is much more emphasis today on manufacturing, the service sectors and personal interaction than on production of materials. The supermarket has in many ways replaced the factory, and the computer screen the shovel or pick. Wales is now a major contributor to the cultural industries.

Whereas once the employer may have been known to the workforce and may well have lived in or near their community, today the worker might be employed by a multinational company with its headquarters on the other side of the world.

There is, however, at least one similarity between 1905 and today. We are, on average, working as many hours every week now as we were then.

SuperTed TV Series production still. Director Designer Dave Edwards

The immensely popular cartoon *SuperTed* was launched by Cardiff-based animation company Siriol in 1982. The series was later licensed by Disney. Today, Wales's vibrant animation industry has an estimated annual turnover of £7.5m

Transport

Rivers and canals

Wherever they were located, industries could only flourish if they could get their products to market. Canals, tram roads and an improving road system provided large-scale bulk transportation and some Turnpike Trusts operated in Wales. It was the need to establish good communication between Dublin and London that led to one of the most outstanding examples of road-building across Wales. The engineer Thomas Telford was engaged to build the road to Holyhead now known as the A5, and his great suspension bridge across the Menai Straits was opened in 1826. His suspension bridge at Conwy was opened in the same year.

The Menai Suspension Bridge opened on 30 January 1826. It was an occasion for great celebration, as is revealed by this contemporary quote:

Menai Bridge *by T. Picken, 1849*

47

Recovering the Ivy May *for the National Museum's collections in 1977*

'At one time the Bridge was so crowded that it was difficult to move along. Most of the carriages of the neighbouring gentry, stagecoaches, post-chaises, gigs and horses, passed repeatedly over and kept up a continual procession for several hours. The demand for tickets was so great that they could not be issued fast enough and many in the madness of their joy threw their tickets away that they might have the pleasure of paying again. Not a single accident or unpleasant occurrence took place and everyone appeared satisfied with the bridge and delighted they could go home and say "I crossed the first day it was opened". The receipts were about £18.'

Telford was also responsible for one of the great masterpieces of canal engineering – his massive Pontcysyllte Aqueduct, spanning the River Dee near Llangollen. The aqueduct is 304m (1,000ft) long and the cast-iron trough holding the water is supported on elegant stone columns standing 39m (127ft) high.

Steep hills and valleys prevented most of the canals of south Wales from being connected together by water. Instead, links with industries were provided by horse-drawn tram roads, some of which were later converted to steam. There were about 241km (150 miles) of tram roads along the northern outcrop of the coalfield. This was the largest network of horse-drawn tram roads in the world.

The opening of a canal was often an opportunity for a great celebration as it meant that bulk cargoes could be conveyed rapidly to the ports.

The canals were known as inland navigations, and the people who built them were called navigators – later shortened to 'navvies'. Their principal tools were the pick and shovel, the hammer and the drill, for making shot holes to blast out the rock.

'It was found necessary to take the canal for nearly two miles through the midst of Crymlyn, or Crumlin, bog or morass, the soft spongy ground of which rising up repeatedly after the surface was cut away, seemed to present an insuperable obstacle to the completion of the undertaking .... The work may be looked upon as not the least striking instance which this country affords of spirit and perseverance successfully exerted.'

Swansea Guide, *The Reverend J. Oldisworth, 1802*

For its day, the speed of construction of the canals was astonishing. Hundreds of men and boys were engaged in the arduous task. Work began in 1790 on the Glamorganshire Canal and, within four years, it was opened between Cardiff and Merthyr Tydfil – just under 40km (25 miles), through fifty locks and rising 165.5m (543 ft) above sea level.

The narrow boats on the south Wales canals were built for hard work. The *Ivy May*, built in 1934, served as a maintenance boat on the Neath Canal until it was recovered for the National Museum in 1977.

'The canal from Cardiff to Merthir-Tidvil is completed, and a fleet of canal boats have arrived at Cardiff laden with the produce of the ironworks there, to the great joy of the whole town .... Nothing appears more extraordinary than, from a boat navigating this canal, to look down on the river Taff,

dashing among the rocks 100 yards below .... The first barge that arrived at Cardiff was finely decorated with colours, and was navigated from the Mollingriffield works by Mr. Bird, sen. water-bailiff of Cardiff.'

J. Phillips, A General History of Inland Navigation, *4th edition, 1803*

Ports and harbours

The ports and harbours of Wales were, in so many senses, the gateways that allowed Welsh people and products access to the wider world, and a rich array of goods to come in.

Sea trade has been vital to the economy for centuries and, wherever possible, creeks, beaches and navigable rivers have been the springboards for trade. Since the Middle Ages, cargoes were shipped to the West Country of England and further afield from ports along the coast of south Wales.

The trading floor at the Coal Exchange in Cardiff, 1912

49

An aerial view of Milford Haven. In the twentieth century, the deep waters of Milford Haven saw its growth into a major oil importing and refining area. Many former industrial ports and harbours are now finding a new lease of life as marinas and holiday centres

Daniel Defoe noted when he visited Tenby in 1720 that it was 'a most agreeable town ... being a very good fishery for herring in season, a great colliery, or rather export of coals, and they also drive a considerable trade to Ireland'. Its near neighbour, Saundersfoot, started life exporting coal and is now an important holiday centre, and it was a similar story in Porthcawl.

The great coal ports of south Wales boomed during the nineteenth century, and grew to be important commercial and business centres. Cardiff's growth was directly linked to the expansion of its docks, and the docks area became the centre for intense business dealing and commerce.

Construction on such a large scale demanded great engineering skills and, sometimes, a very bold approach. The creation of the North Dock in Swansea in 1852 required redirection of the river, and the construction of the massive breakwater at Holyhead was part of the need to expand the traffic to Ireland.

Trade from the smaller harbours was also vital, especially those serving the rural areas. It was quite common for farmers in the coastal regions of west Wales to own part shares in boats and cargoes.

In the mid-nineteenth century, ships sailed from Cardigan, Barmouth and other small ports, carrying emigrants to North America.

Railways

Skills gained by the canal builders were put to good use as the railways began to spread across Wales. By the end of the nineteenth century, lines had been built to link into all the industrial valleys, and a network of railways connected most of Wales.

In addition to negotiating routes along the winding valleys, lines were built across the grain of the land, necessitating the building of massive cuttings and tunnels. As the nineteenth century progressed, so more mechanical aids became available, but most of the work was done with picks, shovels and human and animal muscle.

Left: A Great Western Railway holiday destination poster

Bottom left: David Davies of Llandinam, in top hat and coat tails, supervising the excavation of the massive Talerddig Cutting on the Newtown to Machynlleth line. When it was completed in 1862 it was the deepest in the world at 35.5m (120 ft)

Railways spread across Wales, and the need for fast, reliable communication with Ireland that had resulted in the construction of the A5 road also applied to the railways. Two main lines crossed Wales on the north and south, attracting the skills of two great nineteenth-century engineers: Isambard Kingdom Brunel and Robert Stephenson. Brunel was involved with the South Wales Railway, and Stephenson with the Chester and Holyhead line.

By the 1920s, the railway network was serving many parts of the country. Lines reached into the rural areas, giving rapid access to a wider world. Seaside towns began to develop as holiday resorts, and a richer variety of goods could be transported to all areas.

NETWORKS

The great railway builder Robert Stephenson stood above the Menai Straits and contemplated the challenge of spanning the waters with a railway bridge. 'I stood, therefore, on the verge of responsibility from which I had nearly shrunk.' To make a rail link to Holyhead required a magnificent feat of engineering. His tubular bridges at Conwy and across the Menai Straits are part of the network of railway lines across north Wales.

Another great nineteenth-century engineer, working in south Wales, was Isambard Kingdom Brunel, who was instrumental in creating the west–east rail link and gaining access into the industrial hinterland. His viaduct at Aberdare was a masterpiece of engineering in timber.

Before the railways, the movement of goods was restricted to canals and horse-drawn tram roads, and before them it was sea travel or the appalling road network and dangerous river crossings. In the impoverished mining areas in the 1920s and 1930s, government-funded 'new roads' were opened to link hitherto unconnected valleys. The increase in road traffic in the second half of the twentieth century caused massive congestion problems; Port Talbot, for example, experienced notorious traffic jams when a change of shifts at the steel works coincided with the operation of the railway level crossing.

New road consrtuction between the Ogmore and Garw valleys in south Wales in the 1920–30s

The availability of good road systems now dominates so many aspects of life. The construction of the main west–east A55 road in north Wales, and the M4 in the south, has dictated the development of housing and industry. Our modern life is dependent on the efficient delivery of energy and information into our homes and workplaces. Gas pipes, electricity cables, water supplies and data 'pipelines' are the networks that are vital to maintain our demanding lifestyles today.

ACHIEVERS:
Richard Trevithick

Trevithick (1771–1833) was the Cornish engineer who built the first steam locomotive to run on rails. The historic occasion was 21 February 1804, along the Penydarren tram road, between the Penydarren Ironworks in Merthyr Tydfil and the basin on the Glamorganshire Canal at Abercynon. He wrote:

'... yesterday we proceeded on our journey with the engine; we carry'd ten tons of Iron, five wagons, and 70 Men riding on them the whole of the journey. Its above 9 miles which we perform'd in 4 hours and 5 mints., but we had to cut down some trees and remove some Large rocks out of the road. The engine, while working, went nearly 5 miles pr hour, there was no water put into the boiler from the time we started until we arriv'd at our journey's end.'

The Twentieth Century

Between two world wars

The interwar years were a difficult time in Wales, as the decline of major industries heralded a period of crippling unemployment and depression in some areas.

It was the south Wales coalfield that bore the brunt of the calamity, with 241 mines closing between 1921 and 1936. There were similar stories in the slate industry, as well as in parts of north-east Wales, although here, with the opening of new rayon-producing works and with an expansion of holiday resorts, the effects of the Depression were not so severe.

Picking coal off slag heaps in south Wales during the Depression

Women who had worked at a variety of jobs during the First World War were dismissed, either to make way for men or as part of the recession. Thousands left Wales to work in domestic service in England. Few women had the opportunity to progress in teaching or the civil service because of the 'marriage bar', which meant that a woman was forced to leave her job if she married.

Running a home on a very low level of income and in sometimes appalling conditions, coupled with a poor diet and overwork, inevitably resulted in ill health.

However, by the late 1930s, employment prospects began slowly to improve, with the opening of trading estates, for example the Treforest Industrial Estate in 1937, and munitions factories to support the Second World War.

54

Far left: *A mother and child in Nantgarw, 1937*

Bottom left: *Children on the Dinas Recreation Ground in Rhondda in the 1930s*

Below: *Pontycymmer Labour Party women on a hunger march in the 1930s*

The second half of the twentieth century

By the mid-twentieth century, the nature of industrial Wales was changing radically. The provision of public road transport was enabling more people to travel to centres of employment, and significantly more women were entering the workforce. Industrial estates were also affording employment opportunities in a wide range of manufacturing industries, producing goods that included washing machines, toys, refrigerators, paints and man-made fibres.

The second half of the twentieth century saw a rapid expansion in the building of houses and roads. More people had spare money and time, and new features – such as leisure centres and out-of-town retail complexes – appeared. With the reclamation

Diamond turning at Smith's Industries in Ystradgynlais in the 1950s. The factory manufactured clocks and was known locally as 'The Tick Tock'

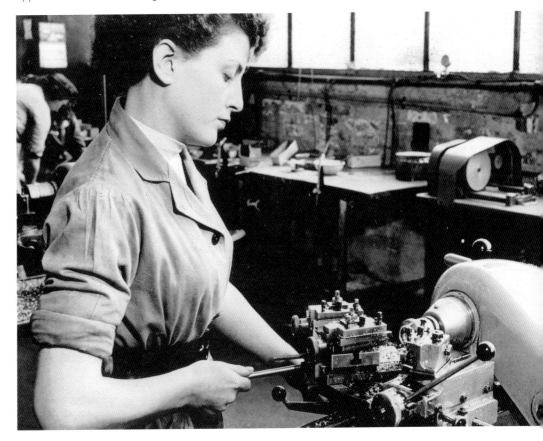

of former industrial land came country parks and business and enterprise parks, all dependent on the use of cars or buses. The increase in traffic has, of course, had – and continues to have – a profound effect on the environment. Every new house expects space for at least one car, and new housing estates are laid out to accommodate access for cars.

The transformation of the landscape

The strip of land along the Heads of the Valleys of south Wales was transformed by the industrialisation of Wales. Even by the mid-nineteenth century this area looked completely different from the way it had previously. The once-open uplands bordering the Brecon Beacons and the

upper reaches of the valleys that bisect south Wales on a north-to-south alignment were filled with industrial activity based around the large-scale manufacture of iron and, later, steel.

The landscape was scratched, scraped, probed and prodded in the search for coal (converted to coke for fuelling the furnaces), ironstone (found in narrow seams, often close to the surface) and limestone (outcropping along the edge of the coalfield).

Metal mining on Halkyn Mountain, near Flint, has left a landscape that is reminiscent of a First World War battlefield. Each 'pock mark' represents a shaft sunk to strike the parallel veins of lead ore.

At the eastern edge of the coalfield, the former iron-manufacturing town of Blaenafon and its surrounding area now enjoy international recognition, after being made a UNESCO World Heritage Site in 2000. In the centre of the town are the

By permission of the National Library of Wales

Crown copyright: Royal Commission on the Ancient and Historical Monuments of Wales

Left: A South Wales Industrial Landscape *by Penry Williams, c.1825*

Above: *Lead mining on Halkyn Mountain. Each depression and mound is a shaft that was sunk to reach the veins of lead*

ironworks, with their casting houses, furnaces and great water-balance tower, and across the valley is the award-winning Big Pit: National Coal Museum. The town is surrounded by a landscape steeped in historical significance, with its remains of early coal- and iron-workings, limestone quarries and a veritable network of watercourses and tram roads. Above the town, Blorenge Mountain marks one of the abrupt divisions between industrial and rural south Wales.

The view to the north of Blaenafon. The landscape is rich in industrial archaeology, with reservoirs, ponds and watercourses. Tramroads and inclines linked Blaenafon with the Garnddyrys iron forge and the canal at Llanfoist

LANDSCAPE

Idris Davies, the Rhymney-born early twentieth-century poet, wrote about his home area.

'On some of the hillsides overlooking the mining towns there are still the remnants of woodland, and the fox is never far from these. I have heard him barking in the night along the hills, while down below in the valleys the hills are lit up ... crescents and bracelets of artificial stars competing with the authentic stars in the heaven. Yet it is not so much the landscape that matters. The essence of the thing is often in its associations.'

Associations and perceptions have coloured our image of industrialisation. There are parts of Wales where it is impossible to ignore the effects of industrialisation, yet there are other places where all that remains may be a few enigmatic dips and hollows.

The lower Swansea Valley in the 1960s was one of the most polluted and disfigured landscapes in Europe, a legacy of hundreds of years of industrial activity. The story of its restoration and reuse reflects the late twentieth-century changes to the economy of Wales. The copper works, railway lines and the massive tips of toxic waste of the old 'smoke stack' industries have been replaced with a thriving Enterprise Park with retail outlets, service industries and a new sports stadium all set within a new landscaped environment. Those processes that gave Wales so much of its character, and contributed so much to its culture, are now remembered and celebrated in the National Waterfront Museum.

The lower Swansea Valley in the 1960s

The same area today

Images © City and County of Swansea and the University of Wales

FRONTIERS

Industrialisation has been a continual process of change, as more efficient ways of working and improved technological innovations have been applied.

The contribution made by our forebears was far-reaching, providing the foundation for our modern science, technology and engineering. Some of the work being done in Wales today by a wide range of successful companies is equally groundbreaking, and often supported by research and development in Welsh universities.

There is, however, a sense of continuity. Once, the hulls of wooden ships were protected from wood-boring worms by sheathing in copper plate. Today, metal-eating bugs are prevented from devouring the hulls of modern ships by the use of chemical-filled sachets that were developed and produced in Wales. The first steam locomotive ran on rails in Wales.

© Airbus UK

An Airbus A340-600 wing being removed from the main assembly jig at Airbus UK's factory in Broughton, north Wales

Today, the wings for one of the most advanced passenger aircraft, the Airbus, are being produced in Broughton.

So many frontiers have been pushed back by Welsh-based expertise. Alfred Russel Wallace, born in Usk in 1823, developed the theory of evolution at the same time as Charles Darwin. In fact, Wallace sent Darwin a copy of his work before Darwin's famous presentation to the Royal Society.

Perhaps one of the least-known Welsh 'frontiersmen' was Robert Recorde, born in Tenby about 1510. His contribution? The invention of the 'equals' sign, now in daily use by millions of people worldwide.

Currently, Wales is leading developments in areas such as hydrogen as a new alternative energy source, biomedical advances and the use of recycled paper in a range of everyday applications.

Wales now needs to identify its future economic and social aspirations, in particular how it will apply leading-edge technologies in securing economic activity. Wales is seen as a nation of great potential, and likely to be a country that will witness frontiers in innovation and development pushed back at the beginning of the current millennium, as it has done in the past.

© National Portrait Gallery, London

Alfred Russel Wallace by Thomas Sims, oil paint on photograph, photograph taken c.1863–1866

Information for Visitors

Contacting us

National Waterfront Museum
Oystermouth Road
Maritime Quarter
Swansea
SA1 1SN

Tel: (01792) 638950
Fax: (01792) 638956
E-mail: waterfrontmuseum@nmgw.ac.uk
Web: www.waterfrontmuseum.co.uk

Planning a visit

We are open every day (except New Year's Day and some days during Christmas) between 10 am and 5 pm, but please telephone to avoid disappointment. For groups of 10 or more, please call in advance to book your visit.

Entry to the Museum is **FREE** and it is fully accessible.

Parking

The car park is on Oystermouth Road and there are drop off/pick up points close to the entrance. There are around 30 designated parking spaces for disabled visitors, plus 2 near the eastern entrance at the top of Burrows Place. There are 6 designated coach parking spaces in the car park.

Travelling to the National Waterfront Museum

By car: follow the brown signs from Junction 42 on the M4. By train: the railway station is in High Street. The bus station is at the Quadrant Shopping Centre.

Disability access

There is wheelchair access to all public areas and lifts to the upper floor. We have some information available in Braille and large print formats, and the building is fitted with induction loops.

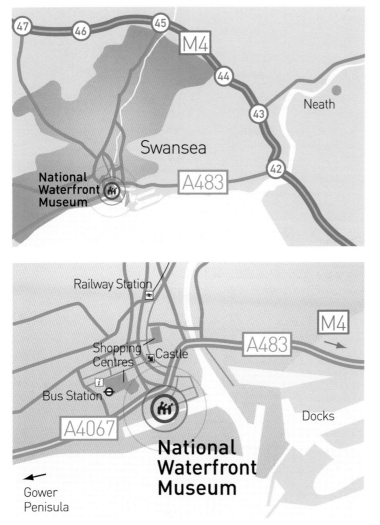

Children, families and events

There are baby-changing facilities and there is open, grassy space outside suitable for picnics. We have a regular programme of events, many of which are suitable for children and families. To find out what's on check our website or telephone for details.

Food and shopping

The café is on the ground floor. We have a well-stocked shop, also on the ground floor, with a wide range of books and gifts.

Learning

We have dedicated education staff and facilities offering a varied programme of activities for formal and informal education. Research and study facilities are available by appointment in our extensive reference library and photographic collection.

Facilites for hire

Meeting rooms and galleries are available for hire for special functions and events.

Glossary

Adit
This is a common term for a horizontal or near horizontal tunnel driven into a hillside.

Butty
This has a dual meaning. It was the term for a personal friend and, in some mining areas, the term for short timber support props that were used at the coal face.

Court of Requests
The Court of Requests was a legal body set up to recover small debts. If the debt was not repaid, the Court of Requests could authorise bailiffs to enter the debtors' premises and recover goods to cover the cost of the debt.

Dram
The common term used in the south Wales coalfield to describe a small truck used for underground haulage.

Drover
As the name suggests, these were the men who drove herds of cattle from Wales to markets in England. The drovers were very important to the economy of rural Wales, until the coming of the railways largely saw an end to their trade. Vicar Pritchard, who lived between 1549 and 1644, wrote a poem giving advice to drovers. The first verse reads:

Os dwyt borthmon *dela'n onest*,
    Tâl yn gywir am y gefaist;
    Cadw d'air, na thorr addewid;
Gwell nag aur mewn côd *yw credid*.

If you are a drover, *deal honestly*
    Pay a fair price for what you have
    Keep your word, do not break promises,
    Better than gold is a code *of ethics*.

Englyn
The *englyn* is the oldest recorded Welsh metrical form of poetry and can be traced back to at least the ninth century. It consists of four lines, each line containing a set amount of syllables and rhyming patterns. It has been compared to the Greek epigram and the Japanese haiku.

Hot-strip mill
A large building containing rollers through which hot metal is passed. The massive mills at Port Talbot steel works are automated, with the hot metal passing through sets of rolls at high speeds, continually being squeezed and elongated to produce huge coils of steel.

Jumper
Used in the stone and slate quarrying industries, a jumper was a long steel bar sharpened at both ends and used to drill charge holes ready for explosives. The bar was weighted near to one of the sharpened ends to aid drilling.

Reform Bill
This legislation gave the vote to middle-class men for the first time.

Rottenstone
A soft, friable limestone used in the tinplate and copper industries for cleaning and polishing sheets of metal.

Turnpike Trust
The Turnpike Trusts were companies set up to administer and repair lengths of road, particularly during the eighteenth and nineteenth centuries before central and local government had responsibility for roads. Tolls charged at gates located along the roads were very unpopular with the rural communities, especially in places where several Trusts were in operation and travelling along roads that were once free had become expensive. A Toll House from near Aberystwyth has been re-erected at St Fagans National History Museum. An extract from its lists of charges on the Toll Board reads:

For every Horse, or other Beast drawing and Coach, Chariot, Berlin, Landau, Laundelet, Barouche, Chaise, Phaeton, Vis-à-vis, Calach, Curricle, Car, Chair, Gig, Hearse, Caravan, Litter, or any such like Carriage £0-0-6

Water-balance tower
Water-balance lifts were used to raise heavy materials in ironworks, coal mines and slate quarries in the nineteenth century. It was a simple process that relied on the weight of water piped in and drained out of tanks to raise and lower wagons. An empty tank of water and a full wagon could be raised by the counter-balanced weight of a full tank of water and an empty wagon.